EXI

MENOPAUSE

with Empowerment and Joy

EXPERIENCING MENOPAUSE

with Empowerment and Joy

A SHAMANIC APPROACH

by Razel Wolf

and Karin Linnander

ABOUT THE AUTHORS

Razel Wolf

Razel Wolf, 66 years young in 2020, has studied and worked with women intimately during the 20 years since she herself began the changes from a bleeding to a non-bleeding woman.

Over the last 30 years, Razel has been studying within the shamanic paths that call humans back to alignment with the plant, animal, mineral, human and spirit worlds within which we live. Razel brings insights and approaches that support women to reframe limiting ideas about menopause.

It is easy to move from feeling lost, uninformed, or unhappy into being informed and empowered about perimenopause and menopause. It is a natural phase of feminine life and an opportunity to reset how we journey onward and how we share ourselves. This book is an invitation to educate ourselves and then to live the next chapters of our lives offering the wisdom and wonder of our inner knowing.

My vision: Individual, natural, shining, coupled with co-empowered relations amongst humans and the other worlds on the planet. Ultimately, evolution for all.

Karin Linnander

Karin Linnander is a German woman in her mid-60s who has pursued a spiritual shamanic path for almost 30 years.

At the age of 45, having recently entered menopause, she decided to change her life and dedicate herself to studying and teaching rites of passage, honoring the transitions in life that have been lost in western society.

She went back to university to study psychology and counseling (M.A.) and spent many years working with girls about their menarche and the transition to womanhood. For Karin, it was natural to move on to the rite of passage around menopause when a whole new chapter in life opens, as it does for girls through their menarche.

The time for bearing children has ended and now entirely new opportunities arise, making it possible to realize one's old or new dreams and manifest them with the inner power of a mature woman. When we realize that menopause does not represent a loss, but the beginning of an exciting phase in life, we can relax deeply and walk tall.

My vision: I hope this book can help bring dignity back to how we menopausal women see ourselves and how we are treated in society.

ACKNOWLEDGMENTS

Our thanks go to the women who came together in Arizona in January 2019 for a menopause rite of passage event. You were so hungry for empowering knowledge about menopause that we decided to share our knowledge with a wider audience.

We are grateful to our friends Anne and Barb for sharing their stories as inspiring examples of how to navigate this important phase in our lives. And to Annette and Rhonda for their words about menopause as a rite of passage.

We give heartfelt thanks to our artist friends, Rhiannon Power, Anne Cart, Bex Creasey and Mel Cupitt who offered their beautiful work so generously to support our endeavor.

Annette Corrigan did a wonderful job editing the text and made it so much easier to read. Thank you.

Special thanks to Janneke Koole who supported us with a Lineage review.

We offer our gratitude and respect to all our teachers and the Wise Women who have supported us in our own learning and growth over many years.

CONTENTS

INTRODUCTION

Dear Readers,

Nowadays there are many good books and other resources about menopause. The topic is less hidden than it used to be, and in some respects, the consciousness of our society is gradually altering towards a more open view of this part of women's lives.

But it is also the case that many people still fear and resist menopause. It is not uncommon to encounter beliefs that menopause is the end of a woman's productive years, and that her fate now is to grow old, become increasingly unattractive, and no longer have value in her world.

A recent study found that less than 20 percent of premenopausal women have even moderate knowledge of the biological changes that may occur to them during menopause. It found that even fewer women carry a positive view of menopause — as a natural process that takes us to the next stage in our lives, granting us new opportunities to take our power and open to newfound joys.

Most of the time menopause is still considered a decline that requires remedies to cure it. It is an unfortunate approach to a natural phase of life, which, as you will see, holds so many gifts for us.

We approach menopause as a rite of passage — a transition from one stage of life to another. It can be an empowered phase in a woman's life, a part of our life development that deserves dignity and honor. We focus on the possibilities and fulfillment that can come with menopause.

We both learned about rites of passage through the teachings of the Deer Tribe Metis Medicine Society, or the Deer Tribe for short, an organization that supports a spiritual path that provides teachings, ceremonies and tools for our human quest for growth.

We are both long-time students of this path, which combines traditional, spiritual, and modern knowledge about the human being. It carries a rich body of knowledge and ceremonies in rites of passage. Razel is a senior teacher on this path. Karin's focus is counseling and teaching about the rites of passage.

Although this book is not intended to be an advertisement for the Deer Tribe, it is our desire to thank and honor the lineage from which the spiritual knowledge in this book comes.

All over the world there are organizations and initiatives whose focus is to implement meaningful rites of passage back into our society. We encourage all of you to seek out the knowledge that speaks to you from any source that attracts you.

The best kept secret is this: Menopause is not something to be dreaded; it is something to look forward to as a time when all kinds of new creativity can be born, bringing joy, satisfaction and meaning to our lives.

REFRAMING MENOPAUSE

The formal definition of menopause is one year after bleeding has completely stopped and then for the rest of our lives. This is a funny idea because it implies we will be in menopause for a full year before we know it has begun! So begins the mystery of this phase of our life.

Much of the information available about this transition from a bleeding to a non-bleeding woman is veiled with negativity and disempowerment. Advertising glorifies youth and demeans or ignores aging. Many of our cultures have forgotten how to care for their Elders with honor and respect, and many Elders have forgotten the power and the gifts they have to give.

When societies and cultures persist in ascribing value to a woman only (or predominantly, or unconsciously) in the narrow sense of her childbearing potential, then it is no wonder they view menopause with dread, disdain, or disinterest.

If productive equals childbearing potential, then that very marked point when a woman can no longer produce a human child will be considered unproductive.

But if we watch the world stage and even some of our own neighbors, it is clear that there is much more that a woman can produce than physical children. And if we look carefully enough, there are gems of truth shining amidst all the misinformation.

We have many image makers living a later life of such power and impact that it is impossible to deny. The overriding insight is that the movement from bleeding, through perimenopause, into no longer bleeding, is NATURAL. It is part of the divine design. And although many women believe that their own creativity or usefulness has ended, the truth is that menopause is a rebirthing. It is meant to be an impactful and creative phase of a woman's life.

We can relate this movement to the cycles of nature. Let's look at the example of a fruit tree. A seed comes from the fruit of a mature tree, drops onto fertile ground, germinates, and becomes its own tree. Eventually it produces its own fruits, which then drop seeds that can become new trees.

When the tree no longer produces fruit, has its purpose ceased? No! It has gifts of shade, places for nesting and shelter, interconnecting root systems for communication, and eventually, even its wood can be harvested for building materials and structures that will live long into the future.

If we can allow ourselves to let go of narrow and limited ideas about what is attractive, powerful and valuable, we can join a growing number of women who are navigating menopause with delight and discovery. It is the phase in our lives when we are meant to give exactly what we wish to give, to offer our insights and hard-earned wisdom, to shine and be fully ourselves.

Let us look at some other information to round out and fortify this picture of menopause as a time of power. We will begin with some information about how the phases of life are approached by shamanic, or earth-oriented, ways.

SHAMANIC APPROACHES TO LIFE

The Elements
by Mel Cupitt

We use the term shamanic to mean the culture of awareness, communication, and connection with everything around us. It includes the four worlds: the human world, plant world, animal world, and mineral world. Importantly, it also includes the world of Spirit, as well as the beautiful planet we live upon — Grandmother Earth.

Some of the challenges we face in the 21st century come from our lifestyles.

Many of us are living in isolation from the worlds around us. Perhaps the closest we come to a plant are the cut flowers we receive on our birthday or the plants we see out our windows. Many of us drive around in metal boxes removed from our environment outside our window. Or we may run from the rain and lament messing up our styled hair. For some of us, our major connection to the mineral world is the road materials we travel on, or the gems in our jewelry.

Some of us have begun to grow our own vegetables and herbs, returning to the solace and connection that gardening brings. But many of us have still not put our hands in the soil for a long time. If we are meat eaters, what connection do we have with the source of this food? We may have pets, but are we really listening to the animals on our planet? As many of the animals are driven further away from our towns and cities, we may have no way to see them other than the zoo or online.

Our multimedia devices now make it possible for us to have little in-person connection with fellow humans — to talk, meet, and experience life together. This book is going to print in 2021 — a time when physical distancing has become an imperative. For some of us, the disconnection from the human world has become even more pronounced. For others, the situation has given us the chance to increase our connection with those in our immediate environment.

If we are not communicating with nature, the seasons and the worlds of Grandmother Earth — the plants, animals and minerals — we are denying ourselves access to very powerful sources of wisdom and guidance.

As humans, we share this grand stage of life on Grandmother Earth. We are all interconnected. The other worlds are natural and can teach us about our own nature. The fruit tree does not bemoan its later days when its role in the great scheme of life has changed. But we humans often do. We have an unusual fixation on youth as the only valuable phase in our life. We often fail to appreciate, from a larger perspective, the shifts and changes that transform the part we can play in the greater scheme of things.

We often laud birth, youth, and a certain degree of maturation. But we often resist aging, which we view negatively. To resist the change of growing older is futile. Change is inevitable. We all know it.

In our culture, we also tend to deny, or shy away from acknowledging death. We think it is "the end" when really it is just the next phase in the spiral of life. Many modern cultures leave us poorly equipped to understand that death is just another part of the whole.

Shamanic perspectives understand that life, death and change are all equally important and valuable. They teach us that it is possible to experience life, death and change in a way that allows us to live our lives to the fullest.

The shamanic ways honor the chronological learning phases of every age and stage. Beginning with conscious conception, birth, childhood, pubescence, young adulthood, mature adulthood, and elderhood, each phase of life has distinct learning periods and needs.

Each phase of life is valuable, but none more valuable than the next. The over-focus we give to the youthful phases of life leads us to view aging as the culprit for our discontent. Menopause becomes the scapegoat for this unfortunate and disempowering view.

In the shamanic worlds, the aging woman is revered for her life experiences and the wisdom she has accumulated. She is asked to share what she knows with those in need and those who are learning.

RITES OF PASSAGE

The Journey
by Anne Cart

What are rites of passage?

Change is an important part of life. To live is to change.

Rites of passage are ceremonies, rituals and celebrations that mark the end of a phase of life and the start of the next one.

In western cultures, many of us have experienced rites of passage associated with some of the significant changes of our lives. For example, when a child is born, some communities conduct a baptism. As the child becomes an adolescent, some religions celebrate a bar-mitzvah or confirmation. And when finishing high school, it is common for the young person to be honored with graduation ceremonies and celebrations. Many of us have experienced weddings and funerals — both of which are rites of passage for significant life moments.

Many earth-based cultures have instituted rites of passage over millennia to mark and celebrate changes in life. The essential pattern of rites of passage has been the same in stable traditional cultures around the world for a long time. They involve finding one's circle of empowerment through a process of letting go of the past and the known; facing the future with intention; and travelling through stages of transition, integration and maturation.

Rites of passage provide closure of the past and allow for rebirth into a new self-image and a new role in life. When a person's community witnesses and honors their rite of passage, individuals can know who they are, and what their place in life is.

Rites of passage punctuate the whole of a maturing human's journey. They can take the form of a moon cycle rite, or a life transition rite. They start before birth for the prospective parents, and they continue for the child from birth through adulthood to death. Even though menopause is an important crossroad in life, we seldom hear of it marked as a rite of passage and a stage of life to honor and celebrate.

Moon cycles

The Deer Tribe shares teachings about chronological rites of passage mapped on a life's journey, which we know as the moon cycles. In this paradigm, the cycles of life last twenty-seven years.

What is known as the Big South Moon encompasses childhood and adolescence into young adulthood, from birth to 27 years of age. The Big West Moon continues from ages 27 to 54. The Big North Moon relates to the ages beyond 54 to age 81. The Big East Moon cycles to what is considered old age at 108 years. The Big Center moon goes beyond the normal life expectancy as an elder or wise one can live up to the age of 135.

Although many humans are now living into their early 80s, human beings have the potential to live longer. Here are some examples of women, who have lived long, productive lives:

Jeanne Calment, who reached 122 years old, has the longest documented human lifespan.

Queen Elizabeth II, born 21 April 1926, is still going strong.

Supreme Court judge Ruth Bader Ginsburg, till her death in September 2020 at age 87, was still fully active in her profession.

The world's oldest model, Daphne Selfe, born in July, 1928, at the age of 90 said, "I don't do retiring."

The moon cycle teachings offer a much broader and deeper understanding of our human potential and point to greater possibilities facilitated by progression through the rites of passage.

During the Big South Moon, ages birth to 27 years, there are approximately twenty chronological rites of passage available first to the parents to support their growing child, and then the young person as they move through puberty into adulthood.

In the subsequent Big West, North, East and Center Moons, there are four chronological rites of passage in each of those 27-year cycles. They mark the significant times in each 27-year period of life and support specific needs at each of those phases.

You can read more about the moon cycles and rites of passage in the books Song of the Deer, *Shamanic Wheels and Keys,* and the stories of *Hyemeyohsts Storm* (references are in the Books section at the end of this book).

Life transition rites

Everyone's journey in life is unique. We will each have experiences in our lives that create a strong impact, that change our behavior, health, or attitude. These "dream markers," as we call them, are life beacons that deserve care, attention, and acknowledgment.

How can you, in your own life, bring consciousness and honoring to the events you experience? Here are some arenas you can choose to bring your attention to.

Conscious parenting

Have you ever considered conscious conception and parenting? There are rites that support partners during their process of deciding to conceive a child and help them prepare to bring a child into their relationship. Parents can also discuss their individual approaches to parenting before they have a child in their midst. They can talk over the important question: How would you like to approach this?

Intentional relationships

How about creating intentional relationships? Each relationship we have, whether it be parent and child, teacher and student, partner and partner, friend and friend, is key to how we learn and grow in our lives. Relationships can foster each individual's growth and create co-empowered relations. It is another key to bringing greater harmony into your world.

Loss and trauma

All of us have or will experience loss, trauma and significant change in our lifetime. We can look carefully at how we might return to inner balance after such an event. Giving attention to restoring ourselves to balance will allow us to continue living with joy, stability, and harmony as we move forward. Our partners, friends, and family will appreciate this extra focus on our part.

Death and dying

Death and dying are a part of being alive. We all encounter it when a beloved dies, just as we must face our own death eventually. It is possible to reframe death as a step in a continuous cycle, as a natural part of life. It is important that we find our own way to experience grief when we lose a loved one. We can also support those who are preparing to die, to find their own, empowered approach to their transition out of this physical body.

PHASES OF THE FEMININE

The Four Phases of the Feminine
by Rhiannon Power

Now that we have an overview of rites of passage, let's look at where menopause sits from this perspective. To understand it, let's first look at the phases the feminine moves through in a lifetime: the maiden, mother, matriarch, and crone.

Maiden

Flowering Ovaries
by Rhiannon Power

The term maiden refers to the time that we begin to bleed — our first moon time. It is the moment when we move from a girl to a young woman capable of conceiving and bringing human life into the world. For the maiden, it is a time of exploration of her individuality, exercising her creativity, and becoming familiar with her body and its rhythms. The maiden also begins her discovery of pleasure and the mystery of her sexuality and fertility. When the maiden is natural with herself, she opens hearts wherever she goes.

It is both a tender and expansive time. Generally, our culture does not give the maiden a rounded and positive education about the full scope of what she is experiencing. But there are many ways we can support the maidens in our lives to understand, respect, and appreciate this time of blossoming. Here are some ways other cultures celebrate the onset of bleeding in the young maiden.

When a girl in Japan menstruates for the first time, her family congratulates her and gives her gifts. O-Sekihan, a special rice dish, is prepared in her honor. The rice is colored red and is only served at special feasts. The table is symbolically decorated with red blossoms and red candied apples.

In Cambodia today, there is still a custom to give a young woman a "moon tree" when she starts menstruating. It is a banana tree whose fruits are reserved for her alone from that time on.

In Sri Lanka, among other things, a horoscope is prepared for the daughter's first "day of days."

Navajo tribes celebrate a girl's first menstruation with an elaborate four-day celebration of family and community called the "Kinaalda." Symbolic dances, cleansing rituals, physical activities such as racing, and a special cake called "alkaan" are among some of the rituals experienced during a girl's Kinaalda celebration.

Even though our western culture may not have given us a celebration or education of our significant life transition at menarche, it is not too late for us. We can take time and space to nurture our inner maiden and create a foundation for the full health that we can possess in our later phases of life.

Consider taking a little time to nurture your own inner maiden. Here are some suggestions.

If you can, find a photo of yourself as a maiden. Create a space of beauty and quiet. Give yourself time to dream into who you were at that time. Consider your dreams, the explorations you took, and how you felt as a fertile young woman.

What was the most significant thing you learned as a maiden?

Speak with your inner maiden, now as an adult woman. Learn from her. And if you can, answer questions she may have that have not yet been answered. If you do not know the answers, let her know that you will find out, and share with her what you learn.

Mother

Mother Goddess
by Rhiannon Power

As a maiden, we are physiologically capable of birthing a child. But we recognize that it is wise to move into the phase of motherhood when we have more emotional, physical, and mental maturity than the early years of our bleeding cycles.

As a mother, we know that we are responsible for the life of another. The needs of our child(ren) take precedence over our own. We step into fully nurturing the beings we have brought into the world. We become home.

Some women are natural mothers and find great love, joy and fulfillment in this phase of their life.

Razel: My own birth mother was such a woman. I never imagined that this role could actually be one of delight. But my mother told me in no uncertain terms that her best and most enjoyable years were when her kids were home, and she was actively engaging in our formative years and growth. I was sure she was just saying this to be kind to me. But she insisted, rather righteously, that this was her truth! And her ferocity about it made me realize that this was so, AND that I was not one of those women.

Other women become mothers out of a sense of duty or a need for identity. Although all women are wired hormonally to nurture, not all women are natural in this role. There is no shame in this. It is important to study our own nature and discover whether we are suited for this role or responding to programming from our society and family.

Some women may choose to mother projects or businesses or become teachers. The roles require similar qualities that mothering another human does — care, consistency and commitment. AND there is a quitting time. When we have chosen to give birth to a physical child, the job continues.

Razel: I was at a recent teaching event on Mother's Day, and I gathered the 60 or so people present into a big circle on the grass. I asked all the mothers of children to go into the center and make a circle while the rest of us gathered around them. We sang to them, a beautiful song of love and appreciation. One of the mothers of grown children came to me afterwards (with tears in her eyes) and said, "That was the most wonderful Mother's Day I've ever had. I felt so honored."

Here are some questions you can ask yourself: How have you been a mother in your life? Who or what have you conceived, cared for, and raised to maturity? How do you feel as a mother? What is the most significant thing you have learned as a mother?

Matriarch

Matriarch
by Rhiannon Power

A matriarch is not defined by age, but rather as the woman who holds a position of leadership in her family, clan, or tribe. When we speak of a matriarch, there is a sense of lineage or passing of wisdom from one generation to the next.

Rose Kennedy, who lived a long life as a benefactor, family leader and philanthropist, was the mother of an American president and two senators.

Matriarchs may also expand their circles of influence beyond family and into the community. For example, pioneers in the dance world Isadora Duncan, the mother of modern dance, and Gabrielle Roth, the founder of 5 Rhythms, were matriarchs of considerable influence. These women had their own intimate families of dancers around them. They influenced countless dancers around the world and passed their visions to the next generations of dancers and observers alike.

Today, as we see women achieve greater recognition of their achievements, more of us are stretching into an expanded vision of this matriarchal chapter of womanhood.

The matriarch is a woman respected and sought after. She looks to her womb to find the strength to do what she knows is hers to do. She can creatively apply her birthing ability to do what she, her circle or community needs.

Crone

Crone
by Rhiannon Power

Most of us grew up with the fairy tale definition of the crone — an old, ugly woman, at best unpleasant, and at worst sinister. But now we can see a different view of the crone.

The old, limited view that the word crone used to connote, is changing. We feel we are in a new era of womanhood on our planet. The discovery of beauty and power in old age is one of the possibilities that awaits those of us living now.

The crone is the archetypal figure of the Wise Woman. In some instances, the wisdom may even appear to have origins in magic that will help others in their own quest in life.

We look to age to bring wisdom to the individual woman, who will in turn share her wisdom with others. Look at the incredible relationships between some grandmothers and their grandchildren nowadays!

At this later chronological age, the crone is closer to death and she can see the veil that appears to separate life and death. It informs her perspective about dancing her life out with power, including choosing death as an act of power.

How will we develop this incredible phase of womanhood now?

PERIMENOPAUSE

What is perimenopause?

Peri means "around" or "about." Perimenopause defines that period before menopause when a woman's body moves from regular to irregular hormones and bleeding cycles. It is a transition phase in which hormones become less predictable and eggs are not released as regularly.

Each woman has her own set of experiences during perimenopause. Sensations, moods and symptoms can shift from week to week or year to year.

The timeframe of perimenopause varies widely; some women transition in a relatively brief period, say a year or so, and others transition for 10 to 15 years. There are no two journeys through perimenopause that are the same.

Productive approaches to perimenopause

In the shamanic cultures, the planet that we live upon is considered feminine in nature. There are so many great books about the differences between feminine and masculine energies. For our purposes here, let's stick with a few defining aspects of feminine energy in relation to our planet, Grandmother Earth — receptive and creative, internal, changeable, capable of conceiving life, nurturing. Masculine energy, which shamanic cultures often relate to Grandfather Sun and is described as creative and conceptive, external, sparking life, and taking action. All humans possess both feminine and masculine qualities within themselves regardless of the gender of our physical body.

We can progress our journey toward feminine-masculine balance with a positive and curious approach to perimenopause. Perimenopause is a time when our hormones are shifting and change is happening within us. Therefore, it is a good time to take the space to stop and consider: How balanced is my giving and receiving? How balanced is my active energy and my inner reflection? How balanced is my breathing in and breathing out? Quiet time to go inside and allow greater balance will support our sense of personal value.

When we can recognize our value, and deepen our inner balance of feminine and masculine energies, we can appreciate in a new way our ability to "birth" powerful things beyond our bleeding years. We can see perimenopause as the preparation phase for the rest of our very productive lives.

In the ceremonial resources chapter, we have placed guidelines for a beautiful ceremony called *Honoring our Last Moon Cycle.* It can be done at any time after your bleeding has ceased. It provides a wonderful opportunity to complete the perimenopausal phase with beauty and honoring. You are most welcome to try it!

HORMONES AND EXPERIENCES BEFORE, AFTER AND DURING MENOPAUSE

The chart below shows how patterns of hormone production change as a woman goes through her reproductive years into perimenopause and menopause and the years after.

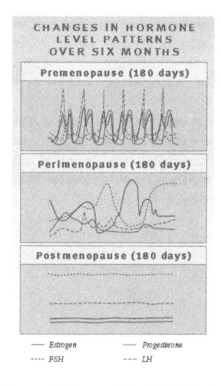

CHANGES IN HORMONE LEVEL PATTERNS OVER SIX MONTHS

Premenopause (180 days)

Perimenopause (180 days)

Postmenopause (180 days)

—— Estrogen   —— Progesterone
---- FSH   --- LH

From Harvard Women's Health Watch, 1999

If we look at the diagram of hormonal movement while we are bleeding regularly, we can see a repetitive monthly cycling. There is a lot of movement. As a bleeding woman, we get used to this movement and we learn about our unique responses to our hormonal shifts within those 4 weeks.

Perimenopausal hormones

The hormonal changes of perimenopause often begin in a woman's early 40s, but they can start as early as her mid-30s or as late as her 50s. The fluctuations can last several years and continue into the twelve months after her last bleeding cycle. Perimenopause is a normal process in the female body. It is not a disease!

Look at the perimenopausal graph. The main observation about this phase of our body's changes is that there is no discernable pattern, from day to day, month to month, or year to year. During this phase, we let go of the regularity of our monthly cycling and dive into the unknown. We are clearly being rewired from the inside out. The changes continue until the full shift from bleeding to not bleeding has happened.

For those of us who like to know or plan or be in control, this stage presents a lot of opportunities to let go. Our body, in its own wisdom, is calling the shots. We can fight it or learn how to align with the many changes.

The first hormonal change in natural (as opposed to surgically induced) perimenopause is a gradual decline of progesterone. Production of estrogen may remain the same or even increase until closer to actual menopause.

The changing balance of progesterone and estrogen levels creates what is known as "estrogen excess". It is not really an excess. It is just that the differential between the two hormones has increased. As the body tries to adjust to the different balance of progesterone and estrogen, we may experience uncomfortable symptoms which can also be exacerbated by stress and stress hormones.

Testosterone levels usually do not fall appreciably during perimenopause. There are more cycles without ovulation so cycles are less predictable. Estrogen levels may swing widely.

During perimenopause, our reproductive hormones continue to play vital, health-enhancing roles. They help maintain strong, healthy bones and resilient vaginal and urethral tissue.

Perimenopausal experiences

During perimenopause, a woman may encounter some, or none, or all of these experiences:

Bloating
Breast swelling and tenderness, caused by estrogen dominance. Relief can come from following a hormone–balancing diet, ensuring adequate intake of B vitamins and omega-3 fats, and decreasing or eliminating caffeine intake.
Cold hands and feet
Fuzzy thinking. The logical side of our brain seems to go to sleep for a while to force us to become more attuned to our inner wisdom. The brain is rewiring.
Heavy menstrual moon cycles
High estrogen levels with lack of ovulation causes the monthly estrogen–driven buildup of the uterine lining to continue unopposed. When the bleed does begin, it then releases a heavy load. It may be worse in

women who have too much body fat (fat produces estrogen). Can be treated with various types of progesterone and acupuncture.

Hot flashes (power surges). Triggered by falling estrogen and rising follicle-stimulating hormone (FSH), they tend to increase as we near our final moon cycle. They can be exacerbated by anxiety, tension, and a diet high in simple sugars, refined carbohydrates, and stimulants such as coffee. Estrogen replacement is 95% effective. They usually go away 2 years into post-menopause.

The peoples who lived more closely connected to the earth did not experience a disturbance or imbalance while moving into menopause. In fact, they had ceremonies to send the energies into their bodies for healing. A story was once told to us that the grandmothers would teach the women to roll themselves up in a blanket to let the powers be absorbed.

Night sweats are on a continuum with hot flashes. They are the body's way of detoxing.

Insomnia

Shifting sleep patterns at this stage of life. Hot flashes, anxiety and a refined-foods, low-nutrient diet can all contribute to insomnia.

Irregular period. Light, short, every three months or more, and everything in-between. If you can live with the erratic periods for a while, they will go away.

Loss of sexual desire, can be caused by a drop in testosterone, adrenal exhaustion, or thinning of vaginal tissue. Check hormone levels first, then determine the best safe approach for you.

Migraine headaches, caused by imbalanced hormone levels. Many women have healed this through use of 2–percent progesterone cream.

Mood swings, irritability and depression, can be caused by hormonal shifts. May also be our inner wisdom trying to get our attention to make changes.

Weight gain, particularly around the abdomen and hips

Menopausal hormones and experiences

As we approach menopause, the hormones produced in the pituitary gland — FSH (follicle-stimulating hormone) and LH (luteinizing hormone) — smooth out and climb to a new level. No longer needed as reproductive hormones, they may now play a role in the rewiring of a woman's brain. She can experience the opportunity to transition from the role of principle caregiver (mother) to her new role (matriarch/crone) with its greater freedom of creative energies.

During menopause, a woman may encounter some, or none, or all of these experiences:

Bone loss, can begin as early as age 30 and can be due to chronic dieting, over-exercising and lack of proper nutrition. Can also be exacerbated by perimenopausal hormonal changes. Optimal nutrition and weight-bearing exercise are some of the most effective approaches.

Heart palpitations, can range from mild to severe. Often triggered by stress hormones and due to imbalances between the sympathetic and parasympathetic nervous systems. They are a call to change your lifestyle and your thinking mind to reduce stress and create more ease in your day-to-day life.

Vaginal dryness or painful intercourse, can be caused by a lack of estrogen or decrease in muscle tone and blood supply to the area. Estrogen creams and visualization techniques can help.

Post-menopausal hormones
and opportunities

After menopause, our hormones typically reach a state of calm. Post-menopause is the rest of a woman's life.

Look at the graph for post-menopause. You will see that our hormones are not gone; they are continually present. We now have the opportunity to reorient ourselves yet again. We have moved from the familiar monthly movement, to the rather random, and at times chaotic, hormonal movement of perimenopause, into this even keel of hormonal presence after menopause. Our new physical state requires a new state of mind and approach to our lives.

SPIRITUAL ASPECTS OF MENOPAUSE

Menopausal Egg
by Bex Creasey

Menopause as a rite of passage

If we look at the definition of rites of passage as the movement from one stage to another over time, from one role or social position to another, then it becomes clear that menopause is a rite of passage. As a woman moves from her bleeding and reproductive stage of life to no longer producing and nurturing human children, it is indeed a huge transition of her societal and familial position.

The role of mother is considered important in our societies as it ensures the continuation of the human race. The next stage or social position is not so well known or regarded. It is the position of Wise Elder, where our title becomes Birther of the Community versus Birther of a Physical Child.

There are many other types of children that women can birth once they move beyond the stage of physical birther. In fact, this position requires some creative thinking and redefining as we re-establish this lost social position in our society.

The Deer Tribe, as well as other schools and resources, offers teachings, approaches, healings, and ceremonies for the transition of menopause. The intent is to re-empower women to discover this next phase of their lives with new verve and creativity, able to give back to herself and her community.

Here are some reflections from women who have engaged menopause as a rite of passage experience.

Annette's reflections

I had always carried a sense of the importance and pleasure of occasion and ceremony. I could easily see that the times of life when women start to bleed and then cease to bleed are major milestones in any woman's life. The menopause workshop, and the rites of passage ceremonies it entailed, were the perfect recipe for setting me on a path of positivity about this great life transition. When I took part in this seminar I discovered that it was possible to write my own script of how menopause would be for me. Maybe I could not prevent every unpleasant experience, but I found a way to relate to all my experiences in as positive and empowering a way as possible.

Several years on from this rites of passage experience, I can see that how I think about my own aging is critical. It informs my ability to take advantage of the opportunities for success and pleasure in this next chapter of my life.

Rhonda's Reflections

It is a return to Ancestral Women's wisdom that knows that a women's worth and value does not decline after she stops bleeding.

39

These teachings are so needed at this time when women are being bombarded with commercial western messages that menopause is something to fear. Rarely do women hear about the magic that comes from being a woman who is no longer bleeding. Menopause is not a medical problem. It is a natural part of being a woman. It is also a rite of passage and something worthy of honoring, not hiding. Through menopause, a women receives a new staff of power to assist her in becoming a Wise Woman, or as I fondly call it, a Crone — strong wise women who continue to birth their dreams into reality.

What we can bring life to now

Most of what we have been taught about being a woman is that we can birth during our fertile years when the egg drops into the womb and joins with a sperm to conceive a child. We pose the idea here that there are other ways that women can continue to be a creative force and birth other types of "children" beyond their reproductive years.

Our hormones have shifted, so we are no longer compelled to be caretaker of others. However, our nature as a woman remains. And so we are free to open to the possibility of bringing life to many other types of "children."

Imagine that once our physical eggs cease dropping, a whole new reality begins. Magically, our spiritual eggs can become our focus for conception, gestation, and life. If we allow ourselves to embrace this imagination, then the possibilities are truly unlimited.

Here are a few ideas of the flavor of what we may bring into the world now that our bleeding has ceased, and we are connected to the potential spiritual life-forms within us.

Creativity

To practice any art, no matter how well or badly, is a way to allow our souls to grow. It is also a way to give something back to life. Creativity is natural to us; it does not need to be forced. We are naturally inspired to create beauty. We can engage in art projects, writing, craft creations, film, photographs, weaving, painting, or even artfully arranging the flowers in a vase each day. Let your inner little girl have fun and be in love with life.

Our Stories

Everyone has stories inside them that when set free, can have an impact. Telling our stories can help us include and connect with others, build confidence, and bring about change.

Storytelling is a skill that can be developed. By speaking clearly from the heart we become storytellers who teach others. We need to be sensitive to know what we can offer. At the same time, we must use our wisdom to understand what stories will not serve others in a good way.

We have included a few stories towards the end of this book. Read them and see if you are informed and inspired.

Maturity

Most people think you automatically mature emotionally and mentally as you grow old. But maturity has nothing to do with age. Maturity relies on the humility to realize that I am not the center of everything. Growing up means ending the excuses, taking responsibility for my life, and making necessary changes. From my naturalness, I can choose freely how to create my life.

How can we mature gracefully? Nature is a good place to seek to understand ourselves. It helps us remember our individuality and uniqueness. When walking in nature, we can be with ourselves as we really are. We can find freedom from judgment and from the need to fit in, belong, conform, and be liked and admired. In nature, there are no rules to measure ourselves by; our guide is our own self-worth!

Our dreams

Our dreams are an important part of what we create and bring to life now. Never give up on what you really want to do, for you are never too old to set another goal or dream a new dream. There is no need to reach high for the stars, for they are already within you. Just reach deep into yourself! Ask yourself: What dream do I have that I have not yet manifested?

Productive patterns

Have you ever changed a pattern in your life that was either merely repetitive or even destructive? Whenever we release ourselves from repetition or destructive behavior, we experience an energy boost that opens us up to something greater.

Our efforts are best spent releasing what we no longer need to think or do, rather than simply pushing ahead as before. We recognize our bottom line when we hear ourselves say, "Enough, no more of this!" and we are prepared to act on it.

We can be in control of our time and determine our life by our honoring our bottom lines.

Balance

Balance is not something we find. It is something we create through the way we live our lives. Whenever we give love with no expectation of getting something back, when we are intimately connected with the needs and desires of our body, when our minds are open to receive new ideas, and when we determine our actions with our inner fire and passion, then we start to live in balance. Living in balance brings us happiness, health, humor, hope and harmony.

Yin and Yang

The balance between feminine and masculine energies, depicted in the Chinese symbol of Yin and Yang, is the key to balance and inner peace. Although they are opposite energies, they attract and complement each other. In our ceremonial resources chapter near the end of this book, you will find inspiration for different ceremonies on how to align with nature to find inner balance.

Ways to celebrate menopause

Never underestimate the importance of celebrating milestones in your life. When we celebrate with others, we can connect with them on a deeper level.

Photos or letters and other memorabilia can serve as triggers for us to re-live our experiences later in life. When we celebrate menopause as a rite of passage, we essentially share this experience with all the women who have gone before us. We touch the timelessness of the human spirit when we too celebrate a rite of passage as some of our ancestors did in the past.

Celebrate with your female friends

Include the ones who are already in menopause. You may enjoy walking in breathtaking nature, a fun day in a spa, or celebrate with a delicious dinner together. Your friends could bring gifts that inspire you as you enter a new phase in your life.

Do a personal exploration

You may ask yourself some questions like: What have I done with my life? Did I use my time wisely? What is my heart´s desire now? What do I no longer want in my life? Why am I alive? Do I experience enough love and joy in my life?

Take time for yourself, write in a diary, go for a walk in nature and reflect, or do whatever you can to connect with your deepest inner being. When you have found what you no longer need and instead have discovered what you want, feel your freedom and inner power and act on it.

Create your own ceremonial ritual

The goal of a ceremonial ritual is to contemplate, explore and transform ourselves. They allow us to emerge with new awareness, support and authority. Most rituals have a beginning, middle, and end. They progress like a story. Structure yours so that it provides an entrance for you into something new.

You can beautify a room for a feast and invite women you like who are already in menopause, and who are growing older with a graceful attitude, with beauty and joy.

The first part of the evening could be a review of your fertile years. Adorn the room with symbols of the creativity you have manifested and projects you have completed. If you have children, include pictures of them. Tell the women about those years – and then say goodbye to that part of your life.

Now express the transformation you are going through symbolically. This is a magical process that is filled with mystery. Prepare yourself — maybe cleanse yourself with herbal mixtures or rosewater, put on a new dress or take a step over an unseen threshold. You do this with the consciousness of entering a new phase in your life. The women now greet you as one of them.

You may then find words, a dance, a picture, or a symbol for the Wise Woman you are going to be. Express what you want, how you want to walk your path, how you want to grow older and how from now on, you want to express your creativity in your life.

Conclude your evening by celebrating together with a nice feast.

SEX IN MENOPAUSE

Young at Heart
by Rhiannon Power

The effects of menopause are different in every woman.

Most women experience a change in their libido, or sex drive, as they go through menopause. Some experience an increase, while others experience a decrease in libido.

A decreased estrogen level can lead to a loss of elasticity and moisture in the vaginal tissues, which can cause pain during intercourse.

Not all of us experience the same changes, and the intensity of the symptoms can vary.

A vaginal moisturizer can help increase moisture. There are many natural supplements you can take as part of a daily regimen that supports and increases elasticity and cell health. For more severe vaginal dryness, your doctor might prescribe medicine or creams to increase moisture and sensation.

Do your research!

The idea that seniors are sexually active often produces a deep level of discomfort in our youth-oriented society and sometimes even amongst ourselves. But there is no reason to be less sexually active as we grow older. It is our opportunity now to reframe sexuality in all ages. Reports show that most men and women between the ages of 50 and 80 are still enthusiastic about sex and intimacy.

How can we maintain our vaginal health during and after menopause? The easiest way is to remain sexually active, for this stimulates the flow of blood and keeps the vaginal muscles toned. It also retains the vagina's length and elasticity. Use your prerogative as a Wise Woman to decide your level of engagement with sex now.

Your 40s are good. Your 50s are great.
Your 60s are fab. And 70 is f*@king awesome.
Helen Mirren

INSPIRATIONAL STORIES

Inspirational stories are often powerful motivators for us. When we feel down, we can be inspired by reading these stories. They help to keep our hopes alive and increase our zest for life.

We encourage you to write your own stories and share them with others. An inspirational story can be happy, sad, motivating, or even tragic. Your stories can lead others to open to gaining new insights and experiences, and learning more about the miracle of life.

My Menopause Journey
by Anne– aged 80

It began in my late 40's when I was in corporate life in a middle management position. I had started to have extreme hot flashes and night sweats. Quite embarrassing at team meetings to turn red and break out in a quite visible sweat. For quite a few years we had been taking winter vacations in the Caribbean and I became worried that I had picked up some kind of exotic, tropical bug.

So finally, I went to my Family Doctor and told him what was happening. He just looked at me and said, "How old are you?". And the light went on. He put me on estrogen (okay at the time – 30 years ago) and everything settled down, until about 6 years later when I was diagnosed with Breast Cancer. Wow, big shift!

In the meantime, I had been re-organized out of the company after a merger, and my whole life had changed. I had started back to university in a Master's Program in Adult Education. I had also begun a Training Program in Gestalt Psychotherapy. At one of my follow up appointments with my oncologist I saw a posting for a Breast Cancer Peer Support Coordinator, whose responsibilities included training, supervising, and supporting Peer Support Councilors. It caught my attention and gave me the beginnings of an entirely new vision of who and what I could be.

From the time I first realized that I was going into menopause, everything seemed to be leading me onto a new "career" path. One much more suited to my strengths than climbing the corporate ladder.

Continuing on this new trajectory, having completed my Gestalt training and earned my Master's degree, I opened a counselling practice and also started doing workshops for seniors. The knowledge, practices, healing and transformations I have experienced since then, more than 20 years ago, have shaped my life today into a form I could not have imagined back in those pre-menopause days.

By the time I was in my mid-60's I had had several falls and at least 3 broken bones. It was found that my bone density had deteriorated into the osteoporotic range. My doctors wanted me to start taking prescription medication, in addition to just calcium supplements. I did not tolerate it well and decided to go off it and find another route. My research turned up the practice of Taoist Tai Chi, so I began attending regular classes 3–4 times a week. Not only did I find that I really enjoyed the practice but also seemed to have a natural ability with the moves. And in a couple of years I was teaching beginners as I continued to improve my own skills. Over the years my bone density stabilized and is now actually within the normal range for my age.

Now at 80 I am in better physical shape than I was in my 50's. I am mentally stimulated, emotionally balanced, and actively engaged every day in my various commitments and activities. I am teaching Tai Chi at the advanced level, walking at least 10,000 steps 5 days a week, and leading workshops in total health and wellbeing, both indoors and outdoors. In this second half of my life I have found that I am a natural teacher, and when I find something that works for me I will likely end up teaching it to others. And in the process the teaching keeps me learning more. So now I am on the alert for what catches my attention next to keep learning and living actively.

I look back and can see now how my journey since menopause has probably been the most enjoyable, productive, and satisfying period of my life — so far. So, in a way, I think menopause is "meant to give us a pause" in our lives so we can re-vision our possibilities and potential. Most of us have a lot more potential than we think, but need something to make us "pause," so we can actually think and take stock. Occurring when it does, about halfway through our expected life span, menopause seems a natural "time-out" point, causing us to slow down, even stop briefly, to look around and maybe strike out in a new direction, and not just keep going as we always have.

The Thing Is, We Think we Have Time
by Barb – aged 67

Some relationships have an expiration date …even a thirty-six-year marriage to a kind and caring man, a devoted husband and father.

It was February 2017. I was 64 years old. "Have you lost your mind?" they asked. "What about your marriage vows? Have you tried counselling?" (Yes, three times.) "What about your pension? How will you survive? You will never find another good man like him! There are ten single women over the age of sixty for every single man! Have you seen your doctor lately … maybe you're just depressed or stressed?"

Three years earlier, I had experienced a serendipitous, unplanned reconnection with my first love. He had traveled from his home on an island, nine hundred miles away. I had traveled one hundred miles across country. We had each returned to our hometown, at the same time, unbeknownst to the other, and for different reasons.

"Hello. How are you? Nice to see you, after all these years." We politely shook hands. Then we hugged, shyly at first, and then

suddenly with alarming intensity. Startled, we broke apart, looked into one another's eyes ...the mirrors of our souls ... and we knew that the embers of our teenage love had never died.

We were each in committed relationships. He described his as, "I hate to say it, but it's more convenient than happy." I described mine as, "We've had our ups and downs, but we've managed to make it work for over 30 years."

Neither of us had a desire to "step out" on our partners. We didn't dare speak it aloud, but we knew our hearts longed to be together. When we were apart, our souls ached. And so, we attempted to soothe the ache by meeting for coffee every now and then, when his long-distance hauling job brought him to a nearby truck stop.

"The trouble is, we think we have time." The truth of that quote for me hit like a ton of bricks, slapped me across the face. What the hell am I doing ... being physically present with my husband, yet mentally, emotionally, sexually, and spiritually absent? I had been desperately trying to suppress this fact for years. But I had no "good reason" to leave my marriage. Now what?

I imagined different scenarios ... none of them had a happy ending for my family. But I could not deny what was rising and roaring inside of me. It left me limp, raw and ragged. My heart squeezed with pain as I faced the cold hard facts: my decision would cause a world of hurt and sadness. But I could not wish away the certainty of what I must do. My authentic self demanded to be alive and expressed.

The next time we met, I said, "I love you. I want to be with you. I want to live in the truck with you. I need to leave my marriage in a good way."

And so, I did. He opened the truck door, and I fell into his arms.

Thousands of miles rolled by as we hauled lumber to California and produce to Canada, and back again. I toughened up enough to learn how to pee through a funnel, into a jug, at eighty miles per hour; he softened up enough to tolerate, maybe even appreciate, lingerie, and scented body lotion in his truck cab.

By day, we "hammered down" the miles, reminisced, shared our defining life moments, bragged about our kids, sang, laughed, teased, dreamed our dream, and cussed out crazy drivers.

By night, we tumbled into the bunk, arms wrapped tight around one another, feeling the feel, smelling the smell, and tasting the taste of each other …. Sometimes with steamy, hungry, juicy, push-our-edges- sex. Other times with long, deep, slow kisses, savoring the synchronization of our inhale and exhale. Always with tenderness, gratitude, and soul-full bliss.

And four months later he was gone. The Royal Canadian Mounted Police found his body in the truck. He died in his sleep while I was in Arizona, preparing for a personal vision quest.

My love was gone. My dream had vanished. I had no home. My everything was gone. Now what?

The depth and breadth and darkness of my sorrow was unimaginable. It numbed everything except my heart. My heart ached all of the time. Emptiness was my constant companion.

I carried the vastness of that emptiness inside my being, inside my womb, for three months. Suddenly one day, I felt a stirring and stretching inside. "What is this?" I wondered. The answer came instantly! I experienced a vivid flashback to my vision quest to a pivotal point during those three intense days, where I found myself sobbing "I choose life!" again and again.

That stirring and stretching inside morphed into action on the outside. To my great astonishment (and eventual delight!) I purchased a twenty-year-old camper van, read the owner's manual, and pointed it south.

"Are you off your rocker?" they asked. "A woman can't drive all that way by herself! What are you running away from? Don't you know that wherever you go, there you are? What are you searching for?"

And I drove two thousand miles. Sometimes I sobbed as I drove; other times I rocked out loudly to tunes on the radio. I drove white-knuckled through the Grand Canyon; soaked in the hot springs of Palm Desert; chanted to the full moon over the Colorado River; camped alone in the Arizona desert and hiked in Sedona. I stopped three times to sprinkle his ashes, and blow him kisses, at his favorite truck stops.

I earned my White Belt, Green Belt and Green Belt First Stripe in Kung Fu. ("Why are you starting this at your age?" they asked. "Aren't you afraid of breaking something?")

New Year's Eve, 2017. I was 65.

"Do you have good medical coverage?" asked the earnest young man. "How old are you? You'll need to sign a waiver." And then he harnessed me up for my first flight ever. I hang glided over the San Bernardino Valley… stretching for more…flying faster and farther than I had ever gone before.

Now I understand the magical transformations that these changes taught me. His death sparked me to life.

CEREMONIAL RESOURCES

How to connect and align with nature

by Karin

Whenever we women wish to find our true selves, we need to go deep inside and connect with our inner truth and wisdom. They are always accessible for us.

As we connect with the wisdom of our womb, we are held and supported by the Greater Mother — Grandmother Earth. We must leave our everyday lives of people and events to access the inner spaces of our deeper feelings, truths, and values.

The most direct way to connect is to go into nature. Nature is our greatest teacher. We come from nature; we are a part of nature. Nature teaches us to become natural, to not worry about what we look like, what others think about us, or whether we are loved or not. When we spend time in nature, we can relax and uncover who we are.

By doing ceremony in nature, we can align with the four elements — water, earth, wind, and fire — and can establish a strong connection with the Earth.

In our paradigm, the elements correspond to our inner qualities: aligning with water can help heal your emotions; connecting with the earth can give you the support you need to let go inside and see what needs to change; listening to the wind spirits can open your mind and bring clarity; and dancing with the fire can bring vision and expand your spirit.

Here are some simple approaches to align with the four elements and their corresponding aspects of humanness:

Water/Emotions

Sit down on the bank of a river, facing downstream, and let go of your heartaches, your expectations, and any emotional issues you might be carrying. Identify them, feel them, and give them away to the flowing waters. Let the water carry away your old wounding. Then turn around and face upstream, opening yourself up to fresh new possibilities and opportunities.

Earth/Physical

Lie belly down on a warm rock or on the earth and feel the power of the earth in your womb, feel her heartbeat, go deep into introspection. Trust your feelings and your inner strength. Find what patterns in your life need to die and what changes are necessary for you to become stronger and more vibrant. Feel the stability of that rock or the earth, drink it in, and allow it to support you to make your changes.

Wind/Mind

Climb a mountain or hill, write down your wishes on paper. They might be a new job, a partner, healing, or the courage to do what you want to do. Then hang the paper on a tree as the Buddhists sometimes do with their prayer flags, so that the wind spirits know what your wishes are. Then let go of your wishes and be open to what unfolds.

Fire/Spirit

Sit in front of a candle or a fire and imagine leaving behind the norms and expectations dictated from outside yourself, as well as those you took on in your past. Gaze into that fire and connect with its unrelenting desire to blaze brightly. Dream in a new vision of your life — full of joy, creativity, energy, meaning and purpose.

There are special times to do your ceremonies that will support your intent. You can choose to do them when the veils between the seen and unseen worlds lift, and magic and mystery are present; for example, at twilight, when the sun rises or sets, at full moon or new moon, or when the seasons change at the equinox and solstice.

Let go of any expectations about what should happen and enjoy your time in nature, allowing nature to reveal itself as your home that welcomes you always and all ways!

Honoring our last moon cycle — a shamanic ceremony

by Razel

Intent

To honor the completion of your phase as the bleeding woman you once were and to own and celebrate the non-bleeding woman you are now.

Items needed

4 red stones (red jasper is a good stone and easy to find)
12 kernels of corn
Large bowl or pitcher of clean water
4 flowers - red and/or pink
Pouring cup
A small spade or digging tool
Compass
A large basket or container to hold all the items on this list.
Optional: a mixture of cleansing herbs — white sage, lavender and cedar — a long lighter, a burning bowl.

Steps of your ceremony

Step 1 — Find your power spot

Find a location outside that is private and safe where you can be in nature. Select a sacred spot where you will not be disturbed and where you will be able to bury your stones.

Look around and take in the beauty or the energy of the space you have chosen and make sure it feels good to you.

Step 2 — Bless your items

Place each of your items into a large basket or container and then:

Lift them to the sky and sun, connect with those energies and ask for the cleansing energy that comes from the sun and air to bless you and the items.

Place them on the earth, connect with the earth, and ask for the stability and nurturing of the earth to bless you and these items.

Hold your basket in front of your belly. Take 3 deep breaths and connect with your own inner resources and the greater resources (some people call this God, Goddess, Spirit, the All, Source or whatever words have meaning for you). Once you have made your inner and greater connection, ask for the wisdom and benevolence to bless you and these items.

If you have gathered the 3 cleansing herbs, place them into a burning bowl. Light the mixture until it is smoking and then cleanse yourself and all the items you will be using for the ceremony with the smoke.

Step 3 — Align with your flowers in the water

Place the 4 flowers in the bowl of water. The flowers are representing your days and experiences when you were a bleeding woman. Take a moment to gaze at the beauty of these flowers. Sense the fluidity of the water, its own type of lifeblood for all on this planet. Listen to any messages that come to you from the flowers and water.

Step 4 — Create your circle of stones

Use your compass to locate the four cardinal directions: east, west, south, and north.

Create a medicine wheel using your 4 red stones. Place 1 stone in the east, 1 stone in the west, 1 stone in the south, 1 stone in the north.

Connect with the earth. As you place your stones, call to the energies of each direction to ask them to be with you. Ask these 4 stones and Grandmother Earth to hold a strong container for you to do your ceremony.

If you have the 3-herb mixture, light it and cleanse the space with the smoke.

Step 5 — Pray from the center of your circle

Standing in the center of your medicine wheel of 4 red stones, speak with Spirit about your intent of honoring the dream of the bleeding woman you once were, and the non-bleeding woman you are now.

Call and pray for the full empowerment of your inner wisdom, ask that the power of your womb will be birthed anew, and that you release all negative programming that shows up.

Take some time with this prayer and expression. Go deep, be quiet. Speak from your womb what you now know. Release what is necessary for you to move forward in a strong and inspired way. Honor where you have come from and dream into who you are becoming.

Step 6 — Pray in each direction

Take half the life-blood water from your bowl of flowers and go to each of the 4 stones in the order that you laid them down. Pour a little water on each stone. As you do so, make prayers of gratitude and release. Here are some suggestions. Please make the prayers your own.

East

At the east stone, give thanks for your spirit and passion as a bleeding woman. Allow your spirit to expand and soar with the eagle. Catch those insights that illuminate your life. Pray for passion and lust for life.

West

At the west stone, give thanks for your beautiful body that held the physical eggs and bled. Go within and listen to your body knowing. Allow for change. Pray for stability and full health in your body.

South
At the south stone, give thanks for the blood itself and all that it held for you. Know there is something greater than you. Simply be who you are with an open heart. Pray for fluidity of giving in your emotions.

North
At the north stone, give thanks for your open-minded approach to this phase in your life. Give thanks for the journey you had as a bleeding woman. Pray to receive open free-thinking and to stay in balance and harmony.

Step 7 — Return to the center of your circle
When you are complete at the 4 stones, sit in the center of your circle again, facing south. Allow yourself to be still and listen to your inner wisdom. Hunt for any remaining feelings of sorrow or loss about leaving behind your moon blood and this phase of your life. Speak aloud those things you identified that you are willing and able to release. Leave what you no longer need in this ceremonial circle you have made.

Step 8 — Bury the east red stone in a small hole
Walk to where you placed your red stone in the east. Dig a small hole there. Place your east red stone into the hole.

As you do so, allow the stone to represent a new seed that you are planting. Release any last giveaways you may have.

Place 3 kernels of corn in this hole. Imagine that you are planting these kernels of corn to be held securely by the earth, gestating, as the new children you will be birthing. Celebrate the children yet to be born!

Take the second half of the life-blood water and pour some of it upon the corn kernels you planted to nourish them. As you do so, allow your-self to dream into the energy that this direction holds and the potential of all the children you can now birth. This is a silent, dreaming time for you.

When you feel complete with your dreaming, fill in this hole with dirt.

Speak these words (or paraphrase them): "Sacred Universe and all that is Feminine. Thank you for my beautiful, female body. Thank you for my years as a bleeding woman. Thank you for the time that I enter now as a woman with new potential for birthing other 'children.' May I birth beauty, power, and my dreams into this world. I have spoken."

Place one of the flowers of beauty on top of each covered hole.

Step 9 — Bury the west red stone in a small hole
Walk to where you placed your red stone in the West.

Repeat all the steps above here.

Step 10 — Bury the south red stone in a small hole
Walk to where you placed your red stone in the South.

Repeat all the steps above.

Step 11 — Bury the north red stone in a small hole
Walk to where you placed your red stone in the North.

Repeat all the steps above.

Step 12 — Complete your ceremony
When you are complete at each of your 4 holes, stand in the center of your circle once more. Thank all the powers that came to work with you and release them.

Leave the space more beautiful than when you found it. Know that this releasing of the old and the birthing of the new is done in beauty.

You may choose to journal your insights.

Allow yourself 7 days of dreaming time, before you speak of your ceremony to anyone. Also keep at least one piece of your ceremony to yourself, which you share only with your inner self.

LOOKING AHEAD

Care for yourself

Taking care of our bodies, our health, and our mental well-being not only makes us feel better, but it also allows us to perform better in the long term. It is not selfish to love and care for ourselves and make our happiness a priority.

Self-care does not just happen; we need to pursue it deliberately. It begins with our physical needs, making sure we get enough sleep, eat a healthy diet and exercise regularly. It also translates to where we place our care and attention.

In our younger years, we are hormonally wired to care for others. Even after our hormones have shifted into the calm stream of menopause, we may still be in an automatic response driving us to give care to others. Although we will never stop caring for others, now it is also time to give care to ourselves.

If you are one of those lucky, elder women who have already figured this out, congratulations! You are an image-maker to the rest of us! If you are one of us that is slower to learn, here are some ideas to consider.

Cultivate your friend circle

Our mothers were largely silent about what happened to them as they went through menopause. But nowadays it is more common to discuss these life changes.

Sharing your feelings, fears and concerns about menopause with your female friends is one of the healthiest things you can do for yourself. They are probably going through it, too. They may not experience the same things as you do, but their experiences can help you navigate what you are going through, and it may validate your own experiences or feelings.

According to a study at the University of Michigan, close bonds between women help boost levels of progesterone, a hormone that reduces stress. It's good to stick by your friends and see them as often as possible.

It is powerful to personally know women who have gained maturity by going through menopause.

Educate yourself

It is wise to do your own research and find out as much as you can about the changes and stages you are going through. We are all different and we need to be able to make our own choices based on knowledge that works for us.

Embracing new opportunities or changing old patterns can bring short-term pain, but the result can be long-term pleasure. When you can live your self-love without apologizing for it, you may notice the increase in security that comes with knowing you can positively change your life.

BOOKS

Books can be a great source of comfort and support when experiencing menopause. Among the hundreds of books about menopause and your life after it, these are our favorites:

The Wisdom of Menopause
by Dr. Christiane Northrup

Dr Northrup's book explores menopause from a medical and female perspective. According to Dr. Northrup, the change women go through is not just a collection of physical symptoms to be fixed, but a whole mind-body revolution that brings us the greatest opportunity for growth we have had since adolescence.

The author discusses hormone therapy options, weight control, moods, sleep, memory, and sex, covering both myths and productive realities. She sees menopause not as a state to be fixed but rather as a real-life opportunity. Dr. Northrup also runs seminars and on-line workshops.

New Menopausal Years: The Wise Woman Way
by Susun S. Weed

This book is the bible for American women over the age of fifty who prefer to approach menopause naturally rather than through hormonal treatment. It describes herbal solutions for many of the perimenopausal and menopausal symptoms women may experience. The author lets the soothing, wise voice of "Grandmother Growth" guide the reader through her own metamorphosis in menopause, as well as offering beautiful ritual passages that integrate the spiritual dimension. Ms. Weed also offers on-line workshops.

Tantric Sex and Menopause:
Practices for Spiritual and Sexual Renewal
by Diana Richardson and Janet McGeever

The authors describe a tantric approach to discovering the hidden gifts of menopause. It includes many self-help practices, meditations, and tantric exercises for couples and individuals. They reveal how to explore and embrace, rather than suppress, the changes this natural transition brings. Diana Richardson offers seminars in Switzerland (www.love-forcouples.com).

Circle of Stones: Woman's Journey to Herself
by Judith Duerk

This book appeared to us magically as we were writing this book, and we both love it. Duerk weaves women's stories, dreams, and visions to open a space for each reader to experience their own journey into the "lost feminine." We are invited to consider our present lives from the eyes of women's ancient culture and ritual. This is the "circle of stones."

Books related to moon cycles and rites of passage

Song of the Deer, The Great Sundance Journey of the Soul by Thunder Strikes and Jan Orsi, Jaguar Press, 1999.

Shamanic Wheels and Keys, Vol. I, DTMMS, 1994, available through https://dtmms.org/product/shamanic-wheels-keys/.

7 Arrows by Hyemeyohsts Storm, HarperCollins, 1972.

Song of Heyoehkah by Hyemeyohsts Storm, Ballantine Books, 1981.

Lightningbolt by Hyemeyohsts Storm, Ballantine Books, 1994.

OTHER RESOURCES

As you search the internet, you may find other forms of guidance, such as seminars, workshops or gatherings, either in-person or on-line, that speak to you. Here are some more resources we value:

School of Lost Borders
www.schooloflostborders.org

The School of Lost Borders holds the intent and promise that one day meaningful rites of passage will be available to all people worldwide. With the present state of our planet and the incredible challenges each individual faces, it is very heartening to witness the global re-emergence of ancient wisdom. The School of Lost Borders is committed to supporting the continuation of this movement and to supporting and empowering guides and colleagues around the world.

The Deer Tribe Metis Medicine Society (or Deer Tribe for short)
www.dtmms.org

The Deer Tribe is an organization that supports a spiritual path of teachings, ceremonies and tools humans can use in their quest for growth and evolution. The Deer Tribe is a modern day representative of an ancient lineage of sacred knowledge of universal laws, ceremonial alchemy, healing techniques, alignment and communication with the elements of nature, magick, controlled dreaming, spiritual awakening and determination.

It has a rich body of knowledge and ceremonies for rites of passage.

Menopausal streaming presentation by Razel
https://friendsofthedeertribe.org/product/menopause-as-a-rites-of-passage-razel-wolf-video-2/

This is a short video presentation that can be shared with friends. Simple overview of a shamanic approach to this phase of our lives.

Artists who contributed to this book

www.rhiannonpower.com
www.anne-cart.de
www.bexcreasey.com
melcupitt@yahoo.com.au

CLOSING NOTE
FROM KARIN AND RAZEL

Dear Readers,

We come now to the end of our little book. We hope that you have learned something, gained something, and are enriched by what you have read.

We are passionate about the gift of menopause — the opportunity for those of us in female–gendered bodies to continue our birthing in new ways. We know those ways can bring us joy and fulfillment and inevitably enrich the world around us.

Please do your own further study and exploration. Find what you need to make this a time of hope and balance in your lives. We, the wise women, are called at this time to celebrate our unique gifts and share our beauty.

We wish you well in your onward discovery and shining.

Karin and Razel